**PRIVATE E**

Scenes You Seldom See

BARRY FANTONI

Published in Great Britain
by Private Eye Productions Ltd,
6 Carlisle Street, London W1D 3BN

© 2005 Pressdram Ltd
ISBN 1 901784 41 X
Designed by Bridget Tisdall
Printed and bound by
Butler and Tanner Ltd, Frome and London

Scenes You Seldom See

BARRY FANTONI

"Have you got some more leaflets I can give to my friends?"

"Thank you – I'll take six..."

"That was lovely – would you play it again?"

"Should we turn it down a bit?"

"Do you know of any litter bins around here?"

"Had your car nicked? We'll get it back if it's the last thing we do"

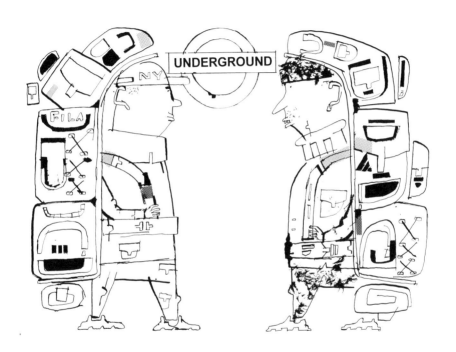

"Better take off our packs in case they injure someone..."

"Your house is fine – you don't need any chemical damp-proofing anywhere"

"I won't bother you now – you're obviously on your way to work"

STARBUCKS

"I know – let's have coffee at home"

"Put your shirt on, mate!"

"Ben's not very bright for his age"

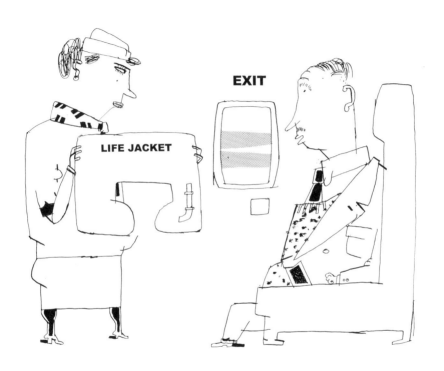

"Thank you – this is most informative"

"I'll call you back later – this conversation is really annoying people"

"...And preferably somewhere close to lots of other British holiday-makers"

"Lost again – and nothing to blame but my own poor judgement"

"Actually, things are a lot better nowadays than they were in my day"

"It says on the packet that smoking seriously harms you and others around you. No thanks. Not for me"

"That's me – I saw the whole thing and can remember all the details"

"Having heard your side of the story, I realise that I am completely wrong and I'm rescinding the red card"

"Oh, hi! Come on in. I've often thought about being a Jehovah's Witness"

"Thanks – but I'm alright for spare change at the moment"

"Just to let you know that we've arrested the man who mugged you this morning and someone will drop by later with all your things"

*"And don't forget to send one to that couple
we met in Corfu fifteen years ago"*

"Yes, okay, I'll have all the toppings... yes, garlic bread as well, good idea... I'll have some chicken wings too, thanks... Side salad? Why not?... Ice cream? Great... Coke... Coffee... Yes, everything, please"

"Hello, it's the builder. Just to let you know, we've finished the job on time and it will cost you three grand less than the estimate"

"No point asking me to taste it – I don't know the first thing about wine"

ART GALLERY

Cafe ▸
Restaurant ▸
Post Cards ▸
Cinema ▸
◂ Posters
◂ T-Shirts
Gift Shop ▸
◂ Videos
Books ▸

"We could just go and look at the paintings"

"Can you stop replying 'cool' to whatever I say?"

*"Hi! I'm Sean and instead of making fun of the audience,
I've prepared some material"*

"It's no good hooting, I'm not moving until the lights turn green"

"And all the ingredients for this recipe come from Tesco's value range"

"I'm neutral as a matter of fact, but I always like Manchester United to win"

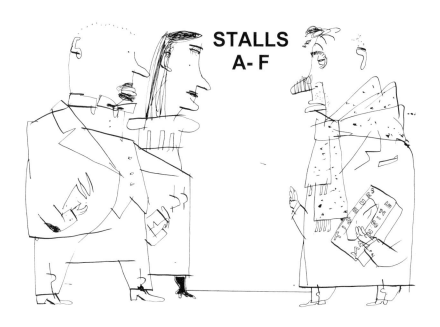

"It will be better if I don't come – I've got a terrible cough"

"Normally we stop serving at 2 o'clock – but it's only five past, so what would you like?"

"Can you put me back on hold? I was really enjoying the music"

*"No worries, mate. I'm a professional barman and know
exactly what you've ordered"*

"The disastrous results are due to management decisions, for which I take full responsibility"

"You are clearly pregnant, my dear lady, have my seat"

"There's nothing about house prices today"

"Nothing with too much bass – I only listen to light orchestral music"

*"Yes, this is Andrew Willis. Who? Do you? You sell double glazing? Great.
Tell me more. I'm thinking about having some put in"*

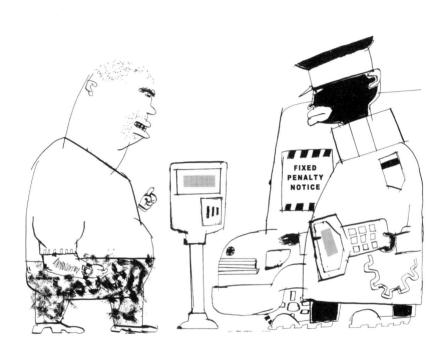

"Dead right, mate... five minutes over is still an offence... let's face it, it's my own fault and, after all, you are only doing your job"

"SPAM doesn't bother me. It only takes a few minutes to deal with and some of it can be really quite interesting"

"Given that I never met the deceased, or had even heard of him until yesterday, I'll skip the eulogy and go straight to the committal"

*"I'm just off for my break, but since you've been waiting so long
I'll sort you out before I go"*

"And there's a big selection of salads, quiches and fresh fruit if you'd prefer"

"I always walk him on the lead. That way there's no danger he'll run into the road, attack another dog or, God forbid, harm a little kiddie"

"Oh, darling, finish whatever you're doing... the World Music programme's just starting on Radio Three"

"Now you ask, I let this Iraqi bloke I met in a pub pack my bag"

"Thank you – and now I'd like to sing 'Summertime', in the right key, in tune, keeping to the melody and using the words the composer wrote"

"No round robin from the Bridgewaters – and I was really looking forward to reading their news"

*"I'm bursting for a piss, but since there are no toilets around here,
I'll just have to hold on till I get home"*

"Homeless? Our son's doing a gap year in Australia,
so you could sleep in his room"

*"You're right, it **is** late. Why don't you go home?"*

*"I can see you are busy serving a customer, Michelle,
so I'll come back for a chat later"*

"It's reopening as a bank"

"Oi, you lot – how about a drink after the game, and possibly a meal together?"

"Smooth classics at seven... Relax... Next on Classic FM, Stockhausen. His 'Mikrophonie for tom-tom, two microphones and two filters with potentiometers'"

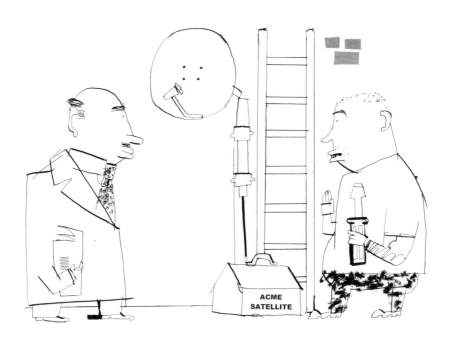

"A conservation area? Sorry, mate, I'll take it down at once"

*"I don't have any opinions, guv, so I'll be more
than happy to listen to yours"*

"Oh, a Nokia 6220 tri-band mobile. I asked for a Meccano kit"

"Perhaps seven o'clock on Sunday morning is a bit early to mow the lawn. I'll leave it 'til after lunch"

"Forget matching the carpet and curtains. I want something really expensive, very big and relentlessly challenging"

"Music too loud? Sorry, mate – I'll go to bed immediately"

"Who wants to watch Chelsea v Man United when there's two hours of canoe flat water racing followed by the men's weight lifting?"

"Over the weekend we went to see the Princess Diana Memorial Fountain.
It's impossible to describe how moving it is"

"He won't stop crying, so I've taken him out of the service"

"Now we've taken Cassius and Paloma out of private education and sent them to the local comprehensive, they really are doing so much better"

*"Somewhere to stay? Sure. There's the village green,
the station car park and plenty of open fields"*

"I've had enough lager already, thank you. And can I have the chicken curry really, really mild?"

"Everything is overpriced round here. Honestly, I'd look somewhere else"

"Well... your previous plumber did a brilliant job"

"Sounds like a cold, but I'll come out and take a look"

"Thanks, but I have all the toys I want. Why not give my present to someone more needy?"

*"**My** children, **my** holidays, **my** husband... I'd so much prefer to talk about you"*

"Have you got something to wrap my used gum in, Darren? I don't want just to spit it onto the pavement"

"There's no programme about Peter Cook on tonight"

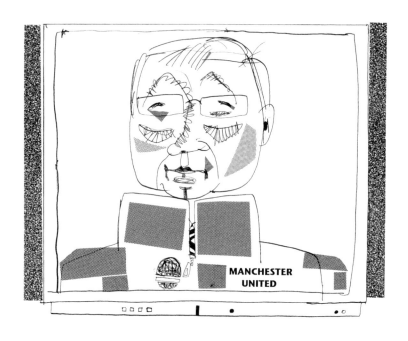

"My player is entirely guilty of the offence and I personally guarantee he'll be punished severely"

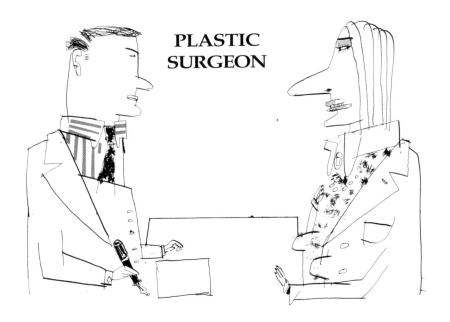

"I'm very happy with my nose. In fact, I'd like you to make it a little bit longer"

"I always say that going to a West End show and having a meal out afterwards is terrific value for money"

"Excuse me, sir. I'm a big Bob Marley fan and I was wondering if you know where I can get hold of some of his early vinyl?"

"I was watching BBC Four last night..."

"Ah! The Duty Free trolley. I'll have a designer leather belt... some aftershave...
a digital camera... the pen set... your desk-standing model of a Boeing 737"

"Here's an interesting story..."

"We had Polish workmen do the extension. They were incredibly expensive and the work was so bad we had to get it all redone"

"A cup of tea? Thanks. I'd like a herbal infusion, preferably camomile and absolutely no sugar"

*"Okay, so we get a few dead lambs and chickens, but a fox
has to survive just like the rest of us"*

*"He's useless with computers. I'm always having
to show him what to do"*